THE FASTEST
DINOSAURS

BY 'DINO' DON LESSEM
ILLUSTRATIONS BY JOHN BINDON

Lerner

LERNER BOOKS • LONDON • NEW YORK • MINNEAPOLIS

To Emily Lessem, my favourite niece

First published in the United Kingdom in 2009 by
Lerner Books,
Dalton House,
60 Windsor Avenue,
London SW19 2RR

Website address: www.lernerbooks.co.uk

This edition was updated and edited for UK publication by Discovery Books Ltd.,
First Floor, 2 College Street, Ludlow, Shropshire SY8 1AN

Words in **bold type** are explained in the glossary on page 32.

British Library Cataloguing in Publication Data

Lessem, Don
  The cleverest dinosaurs. - 2nd ed. - (Meet the dinosaurs)
  1. Dinosaurs - Behavior - Juvenile literature 2. Dinosaurs
  - Juvenile literature
  I. Title
  567.9

ISBN-13: 978 0 7613 4345 5

Printed in Singapore.

TABLE OF CONTENTS

MEET THE CLEVEREST DINOSAURS

WELCOME, DINOSAUR FANS!

I'm 'Dino' Don. I LOVE dinosaurs. I especially like the clever ones that remind us how special dinosaurs were. Dinosaurs were the most intelligent animals of their time. Here are some fast facts on the cleverest dinosaurs that you'll meet in this book. Have fun!

DEINONYCHUS
Length: 3.5 metres
Home: western North America
Time: 115 million years ago

GALLIMIMUS
Length: 5 metres
Home: central Asia
Time: 70 million years ago

GIGANOTOSAURUS
Length: 14 metres
Home: southern South America
Time: 100 million years ago

LEAELLYNASAURA
Length: 2 metres
Home: Australia
Time: 110 million years ago

MICRORAPTOR
Length: 50 centimetres
Home: Asia
Time: 124 million years ago

TROODON
Length: 2 metres
Home: western North America
Time: 76 million years ago

TYRANNOSAURUS REX
Length: 12 metres
Home: western North America
Time: 65 million years ago
Nickname: *T rex*

HOW CLEVER WERE THE DINOSAURS?

The sun is going down over a forest in western North America. It is 76 million years ago. In the dim light, two young *Troodon* dinosaurs are scraping at a hole in the ground. With nimble hands, they dig quickly.

They take turns digging deep into the hole.
A mouse-like creature darts out. With sharp
eyesight and fast fingers, one *Troodon*
grabs it. The small animal is dinner for
these clever dinosaurs.

THE TIME OF THE CLEVEREST DINOSAURS

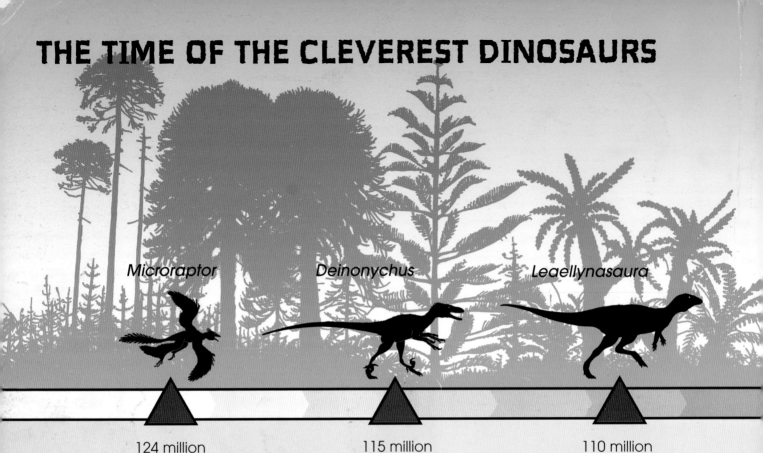

Microraptor

Deinonychus

Leaellynasaura

124 million
years ago

115 million
years ago

110 million
years ago

Troodon and other dinosaurs lived on land millions of years ago. They were related to reptiles, such as lizards, alligators and tortoises. Dinosaurs laid eggs, but they were not reptiles. Dinosaurs were their own special group.

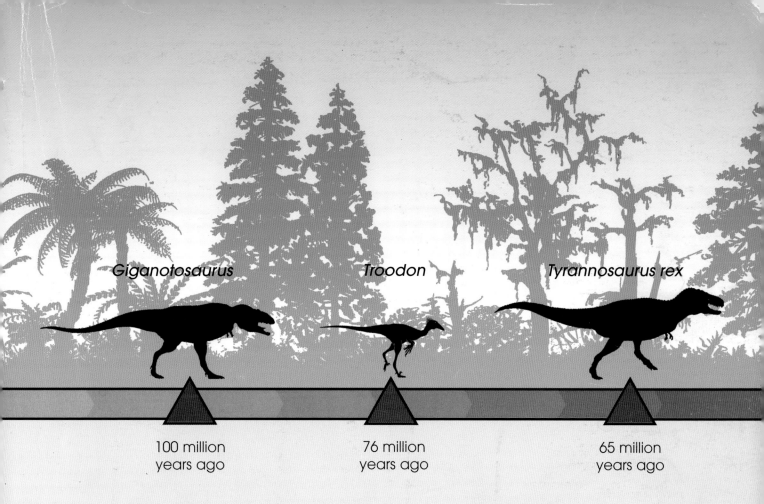

Giganotosaurus

Troodon

Tyrannosaurus rex

100 million
years ago

76 million
years ago

65 million
years ago

Most dinosaurs were much larger than
reptiles. Scientists think that dinosaurs were
more intelligent too. Dinosaurs died out, or
became **extinct,** 65 million years ago, but
reptiles are still alive.

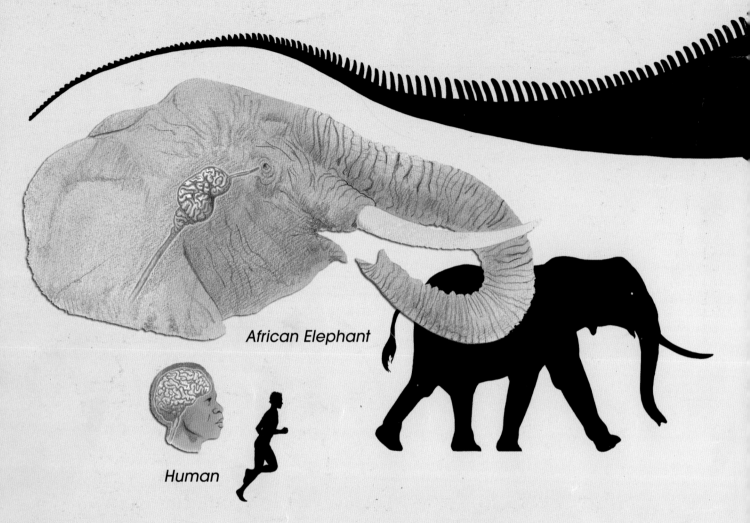

African Elephant

Human

How do we know that some dinosaurs were more intelligent than other animals? We can only guess. To guess how clever an animal is, scientists compare the size of its brain to the size of its body.

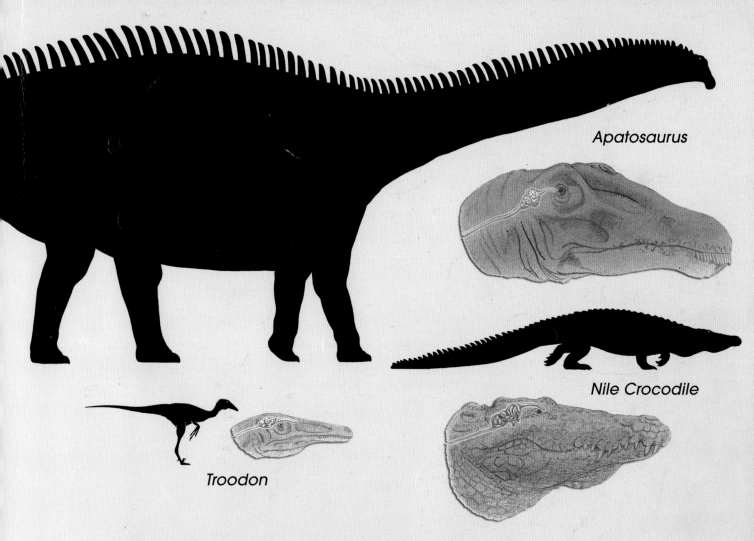

Apatosaurus

Nile Crocodile

Troodon

Humans have large brains. Elephants have
even larger brains. This doesn't mean that
elephants are cleverer than we are.
Elephants have big brains in big bodies.
Humans have big brains in smaller bodies.
So we are more intelligent than elephants.

How do scientists know how big a
dinosaur's brain was? They study the
fossils, or remains, that dinosaurs left
behind. Fossils can be bones, teeth, claws,
eggs and even dinosaur poo.

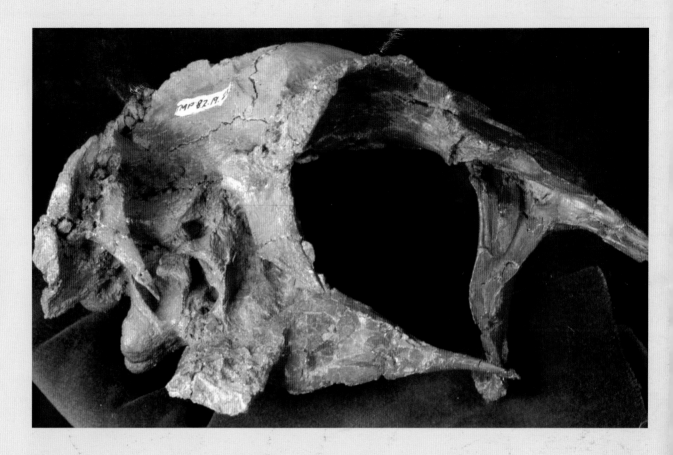

Soft body parts, such as brains, do not turn into fossils. But sometimes a fossil of a dinosaur's **skull** is found. Inside is the bony **braincase.** The braincase is the part of the skull that holds the brain. The shape of the braincase shows how large the dinosaur's brain was.

DINOSAUR FOSSIL FINDS

The numbers on the map on page 15 show some of the places where people have found fossils of the dinosaurs in this book. You can match each number on the map to the name and picture of the dinosaurs on this page.

1. Deinonychus   **2. Gallimimus**   **3. Giganotosaurus**   **4. Leaellynasaura**

5. Microraptor   **6. Troodon**   **7. Tyrannosaurus rex**

We find dinosaur fossils all over the world, but dinosaur skulls and braincases are rarely found. In 1987, a fossil hunter made an exciting discovery in western Canada. He found the braincase of a *Troodon*.

14

Troodon was a small meat-eating dinosaur
no bigger than a large poodle. Its big
braincase proved that it had a large brain.
In fact, *Troodon* is the cleverest dinosaur that
we know of.

BIG BRAINS

Tyrannosaurus rex was one of the cleverest dinosaurs. It had a bigger brain than ours. *T rex* also had a huge body, so it wasn't as clever as we are. However, it was probably more intelligent than the animals it hunted.

It is likely that *T rex* used its big brain to
help it find food or spot **prey**, the animals it
killed and ate. These two *T rex* have
teamed up to kill a duck-billed dinosaur.
They will probably end up fighting each
other for the food.

Little *Leaellynasaura* are searching for food in the dim light. It is dark for much of the year where they live, near Antarctica. However, with their big, sharp eyes, these plant eaters can find food even in the darkness of winter.

Dinosaurs could see much better than many other animals. In *Leaellynasaura,* the part of the brain that helps the eyes to see was very big. Seeing better helped *Leaellynasaura* live through the dark winter.

A *Giganotosaurus* roams the forests of South America. It senses the odour of rotting meat. The body of a huge dead dinosaur lies by a stream. It would smell terrible to us, but the meat smells good to this hungry *Giganotosaurus.*

Giganotosaurus could recognize many smells. A large area of its brain was used for smelling. *Giganotosaurus* could sniff out other dinosaurs, living or dead, from far away.

It is early morning in a hot desert in Asia 70 million years ago. *Tarbosaurus*, a close cousin of *T rex*, attacks a pack of ostrich-like dinosaurs. However, these scared *Gallimimus* can run very fast. They soon outrun the tired *Tarbosaurus*.

Gallimimus was one of the fastest dinosaurs.
It had a light body and long legs. But
running takes more than legs. Brainpower is
needed to control how the legs move. The
large brain of *Gallimimus* helped it to run.

A pack of swift *Deinonychus* is hunting.
These killers are known for their sharp
claws. They surprise a large plant eater.
It fights back, hitting members of the pack
so hard that it kills some of them. The
hunters continue attacking. They slash, kick,
swipe and bite until they win.

Killers like *Deinonychus* and *Velociraptor*
were among the cleverest of all dinosaurs.
They might have worked together to sneak
up on and surround their prey. That kind of
teamwork takes brainpower.

A young *Troodon* practises its hunting skills
by chasing a moth. The moth flutters just
over its head. *Troodon* tries to guess where
it will dart next. SNAP! At last, the patient
dinosaur succeeds in catching its prey.

To catch food, dinosaurs had to make their claws move as fast as their jaws. *Troodon* could grip animals with its fingers in the same way we hold things with our thumb and fingers. It takes a big brain to do that!

WHICH DINOSAURS WERE THE CLEVEREST?

A strange little dinosaur is on the run from a much bigger dinosaur. The tiny dinosaur runs down a hill. Suddenly, it spreads its arms and takes off into the air, gliding to safety.

This little dinosaur is named *Microraptor*. It had feathers on each of its four limbs. We don't know for certain that *Microraptor* flew, but it could have used its big brain to help it move quickly. *Microraptor* might have been the cleverest dinosaur of all.

How clever would dinosaurs be if they hadn't died out? One scientist imagined that they would have been like humans. He made a model of a super-clever animal called dinosauroid. However, dinosaurs and humans are not closely related. Few scientists think that dinosaurs would be so human-like.

The cleverest dinosaurs may still be living. Birds are close relatives of meat-eating dinosaurs. An ostrich is about as clever as the cleverest dinosaurs. Its brain is big compared to the size of its body. So when you imagine how intelligent the cleverest dinosaurs were, think of ostriches.

GLOSSARY

braincase: the part of the skull that holds the brain

extinct: when no members of a kind of animal or plant are living

fossils: the remains, tracks or traces of something that lived a long time ago

prey: animals that other animals hunt and eat

skull: the bony part of the head

INDEX

Text copyright © 2005 by Dino Don, Inc.
Illustrations copyright © 2005 by John Bindon
First published in the United States of America in 2005
Photographs courtesy of: Dino Don, Inc., p 12; Dr Philip Currie, Royal Tyrrell Museum of Palaeontology, Drumheller, Alberta, Canada, p 13; Photographed by Robert Fillion. Reproduced with permission of the Canadian Museum of Nature, Ottawa, Canada, p 30; Animals, Animals © OSF/BARTLETT, D&J, p 31.